A New Baby!

Written by Roderick Hunt

Illustrated by Alex Brychta

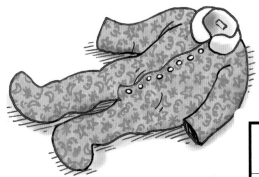

OXFORD
UNIVERSITY PRESS

Kipper's friend Sam had some news. "My dad's away," he said. "He's asked me to look after Mummy with the new baby coming."

After school, Kipper asked Mum if Sam could come and play.

"Yes, if his mummy doesn't mind," said Mum.

Sam's mummy was expecting a baby. She looked hot and tired. Sam's little brother, Leo, was crying and pulling her arm.

"The baby is due in five weeks," said Sam's mummy.
She looked at Leo. "Because his dad is away and I'm
having a baby, Leo is a bit upset."

7

"You need a rest," said Mum. "Come and have supper with us. Leo can watch a DVD while Sam plays with Kipper."

At the Robinson's house, Sam's mummy gave a gasp and held her tummy. "Oh no!" she said. "I think the baby is coming."

Mum phoned the hospital. A paramedic arrived. He looked at Sam's mummy and said, "I think you had better go to hospital."

As Sam's mummy got into the ambulance, Mum said, "Don't worry about Sam and Leo. They can stay with us. They will be fine."

"We must look after Leo," said Mum. "He's only little."

So Chip read him his favourite story before Mum put him to bed.

The next day, Mum had news for Sam and Leo. "Mummy has had the baby," she said. "You've got a little sister. Isn't that fantastic news?"

"Your sister was keen to be born," said Mum, "so just to help her get used to the world, she's in a special baby care unit."

"Mummy has sent me a picture of her to show you," said Mum. "See! Here she is, all safe and snug in her special bed. It has a cover to keep her nice and warm."

Sam's dad phoned. "I'm on my way home," he said. "I'm sorry I'm not with you, but we can see Mummy and the baby tomorrow."

Mum took Sam and Leo into town. Sam chose a sleep suit for his new sister and Leo chose a mobile to hang over her cot.

Biff had a good idea. "Let's make a book to welcome the baby home. We can put pictures and photos in it and show today's news."

They made a scrapbook. It had a page for everyone's
hand prints. Sam took photos and Leo drew a picture. "It's
Mummy's new baby," he said.

Sam's dad arrived. He loved the book they had made. "Let's put the baby's name on it," he said. "What do you think of Ellie as a name?"

The next day they went to see Ellie. "She's so tiny,"
said Sam. "How long until Ellie comes home?"

"Not too long," said Sam's mummy.

It was time for Ellie to come home. "Mummy will be busy looking after her at first," said Sam's dad, "but she still loves you just as much."

Sam and Leo gave Ellie the book they had made,
and there was a surprise for them. "Presents from Ellie,"
Mummy said.

23

"You can help give Ellie her first bath," said Dad. "Just wash her very gently. Then we can dry her and see if she'll go to sleep."

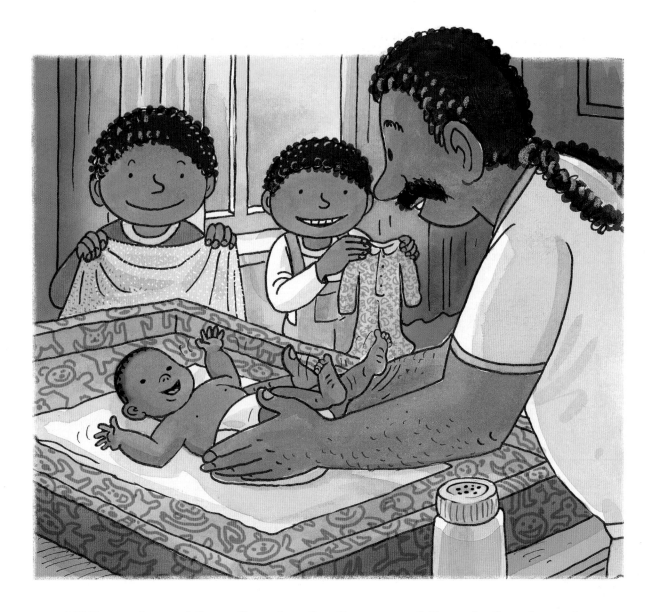

Ellie enjoyed her first bath. Sam and Leo helped to dry her. Then Leo said "can we put her in the new sleep suit?"

"Look at her," said Sam. "Fast asleep in her new sleep suit."

"And she can look at her mobile when she wakes up," said Leo.

Talk about the story

Why was Leo so upset?

What was done to make the new baby safe just after she was born?

How did Sam and Leo feel when they were bathing baby Ellie?

What will you do to get ready for a new baby in your family?

27

Welcome to Your World!

Here are some of the things that Sam and Leo put in Ellie's Welcome to Your World book.

Make a Welcome to Your World book for your new baby.
Here are some other ideas.

What else could you put in?

Spot the difference

Spot the five differences in the pictures of the two mobiles.

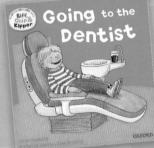
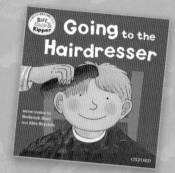

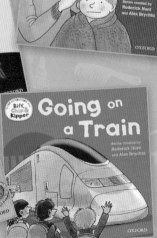

Read with Biff, Chip and Kipper

The UK's best-selling home reading series

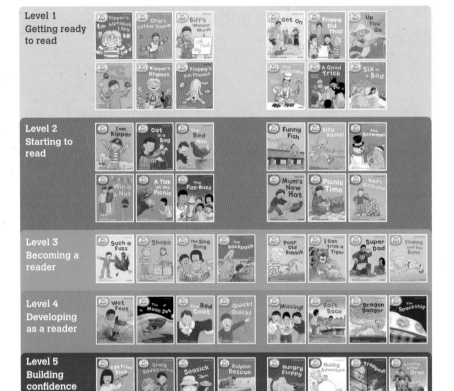

	Phonics	First Stories
Level 1 Getting ready to read	Kipper's Alphabet I Spy; Chip's Letter Sounds; Biff's Wonder Words; Kipper's Rhymes; Floppy's Fun Phonics	Get On; Floppy Did This!; Up You Go; The Pancake; A Good Trick; Six in a Bed
Level 2 Starting to read	I am Kipper; Cat in a Bag; The Red Hen; Win a Nut; A Yak at the Picnic; The Fizz-Buzz	Funny Fish; Silly Races!; The Snowman; Mum's New Hat; Picnic Time; Dad's Birthday
Level 3 Becoming a reader	Such a Fuss; Shops; The Sing Song; The Backpack	Poor Old Rabbit; I Can Trick a Tiger; Super Dad; Floppy and the Bone
Level 4 Developing as a reader	Wet Feet; The Moon Jet; The Red Coat; Quick! Quick!	Missing!; The Raft Race; Dragon Danger; The Spaceship
Level 5 Building confidence in reading	Egg fried Rice; Craig Saves the Day; Seasick; Dolphin Rescue	Hungry Floppy; Husky Adventure; Trapped!; Looking after Gran
Level 6 Reading with confidence	Gran's New Blue Shoes; Ice City; Save Pudding Wood; Uncle Max	Hairy-Scary Monster; Mountain Rescue; The Lost Voice; Secret of the Sands

Phonics stories help children practise their sounds and letters, as they learn to do in school.

First stories have been specially written to provide practice in reading everyday language.

OXFORD
UNIVERSITY PRESS

Great Clarendon Street, Oxford OX2 6DP
Text © Roderick Hunt 2013
Illustrations © Alex Brychta 2013
First published 2013
10 9 8 7 6 5 4

Series Editors: Annemarie Young
British Library Cataloguing in Publication Data available
ISBN: 978-0-19-273515-7
Printed in China by Leo Paper Products Ltd
The characters in this work are the original creation of Roderick Hunt and Alex Brychta who retain copyright in the characters.
With thanks to the Oxford University Hospitals Newborn Care Unit